EASIEST
KEYBOARD
COLLECTION

Best Of
Elton John

WISE PUBLICATIONS
part of The Music Sales Group
London/New York/Paris/Sydney/Copenhagen/Berlin/Madrid/Tokyo

Published by
Wise Publications

Exclusive Distributors:
Music Sales Limited
14-15 Berners Street,
London W1T 3LJ, UK.
Music Sales Pty Limited
120 Rothschild Avenue,
Rosebery, NSW 2018,
Australia.

Order No. AM988867
ISBN 1-84609-871-8
This book © Copyright 2006 Wise Publications.

Compiled by Nick Crispin.
Edited by Heather Slater.
Music arranged by Vasco Hexel.
Music processed by Paul Ewers Music Design.

Printed in the EU.

Photograph courtesy of istockphoto

Your Guarantee of Quality
As publishers, we strive to produce every book to the highest
commercial standards.
The music has been freshly engraved and the book has been carefully
designed to minimise awkward page turns and to make playing from
it a real pleasure.
Particular care has been given to specifying acid-free, neutral-sized
paper made from pulps which have not been elemental chlorine
bleached. This pulp is from farmed sustainable forests and was
produced with special regard for the environment.
Throughout, the printing and binding have been planned to ensure
a sturdy, attractive publication which should give years of enjoyment.
If your copy fails to meet our high standards, please inform us and
we will gladly replace it.

www.musicsales.com

Contents

Believe 4

The Bitch Is Back 6

Blue Eyes 8

The Bridge 10

Don't Let The Sun Go Down On Me 12

Electricity 14

Empty Garden 16

Healing Hands 18

I Want Love 20

Indian Sunset 22

Kiss The Bride 24

Levon 26

The One 28

Part-Time Love 30

Philadelphia Freedom 32

Sad Songs (Say So Much) 34

Someone Saved My Life Tonight 36

Something About The Way You Look Tonight 38

Sorry Seems To Be The Hardest Word 40

This Train Don't Stop There Anymore 42

Tiny Dancer 44

You Gotta Love Someone 46

BELIEVE

Words & Music by Elton John & Bernie Taupin

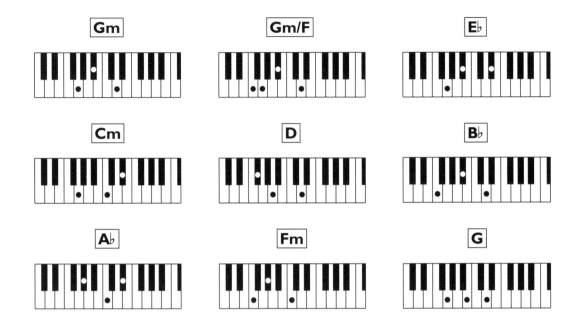

Voice: **Tenor Saxophone**

Rhythm: **Slow Rock**

Tempo: ♩ = 68

I be-lieve in love, it's all we got.__ Love has no boun-daries,__ costs

no-thing to touch.__ War makes mo-ney,__ can-cer sleeps._

curled up in my fa-ther and that means some-thing to me.__ Church-es and dic-ta-tors,__

THE BITCH IS BACK

Words & Music by Elton John & Bernie Taupin

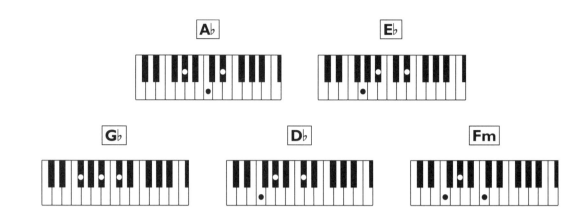

Voice: **Alto Saxophone**

Rhythm: **Hard Rock**

Tempo: ♩ = 132

I was jus-ti-fied when I was five, Rais-ing cane, I spit in your eye. Times are chang-ing, now the poor get fat but the fe-ver's gon-na catch you when the bitch gets back. Eat meat on a Fri-day that's al-right. E-ven like steak on a Sa-tur-day night. I can bitch the best at your so-cial dos. I get

BLUE EYES

Words & Music by Elton John & Gary Osborne

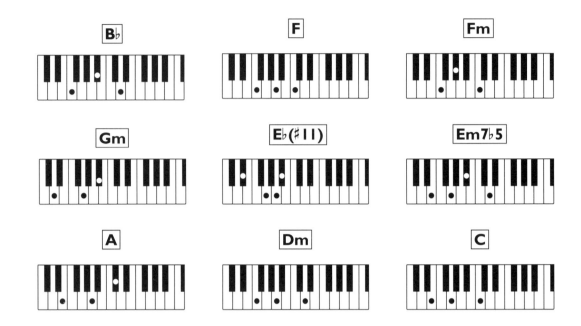

Voice: **Strings**

Rhythm: **Pop Ballad**

Tempo: ♩. = **72**

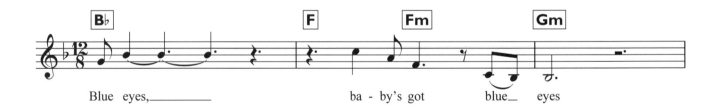

Blue eyes,_____ ba - by's got blue___ eyes

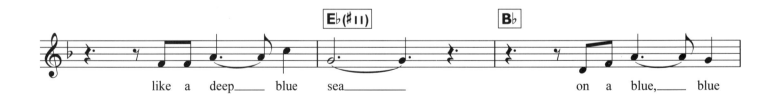

like a deep___ blue sea_____ on a blue,___ blue

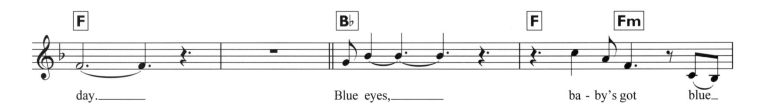

day._____ Blue eyes,_____ ba - by's got blue___

eyes. When the morn - ing comes_____

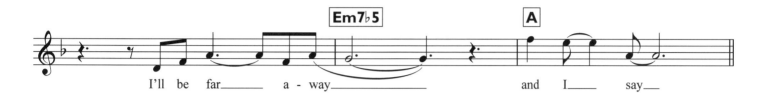

I'll be far_____ a - way_____ and I__ say__

Blue eyes hold - ing back the tears, hold - ing back_____ the pain._____

Ba - by's got blue__ eyes and I am home,_____

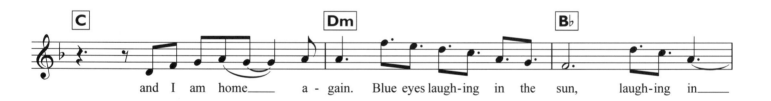

and I am home_____ a - gain. Blue eyes laugh - ing in the sun, laugh - ing in_____

__ the rain._____ Ba - by's got blue__ eyes and I

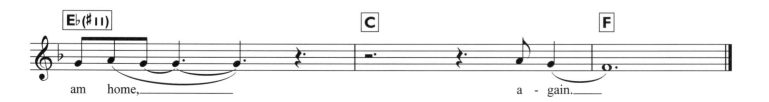

am home,_____ a - gain._____

THE BRIDGE

Words & Music by Elton John & Bernie Taupin

DON'T LET THE SUN GO DOWN ON ME

Words & Music by Elton John & Bernie Taupin

ELECTRICITY

Words by Lee Hall & Music by Elton John

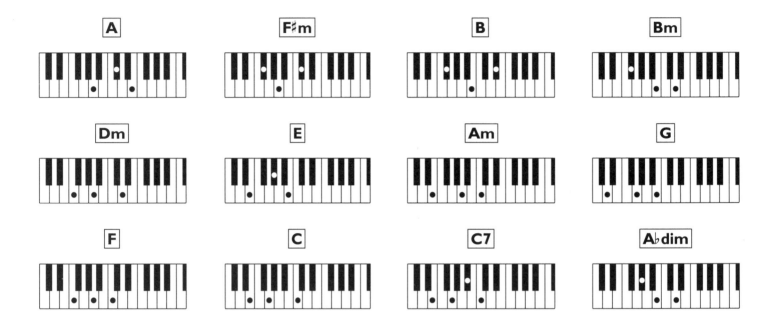

Voice: **Flute**

Rhythm: **Straight Rock**

Tempo: ♩ = 68

I can't real-ly ex-plain it. I have-n't got___ the words.___ It's a

feel-ing that you can't con-trol._____ I sup-pose it's like for-get-ting,

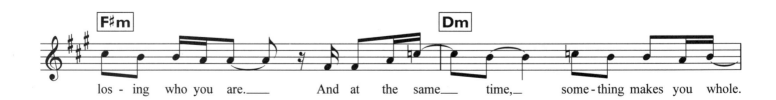

los-ing who you are.___ And at the same___ time,___ some-thing makes you whole.

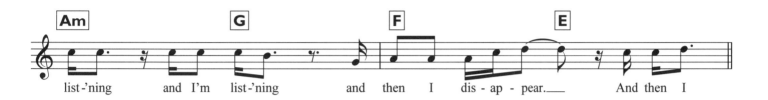

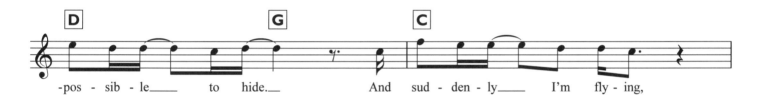

EMPTY GARDEN

Words & Music by Elton John & Bernie Taupin

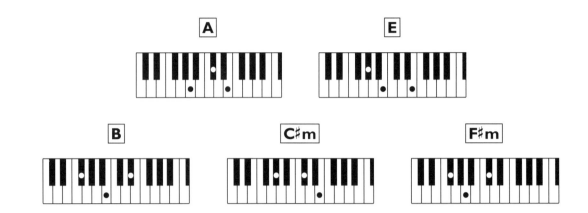

Voice: **Electric Piano**

Rhythm: **Slow Rock**

Tempo: ♩ = 55

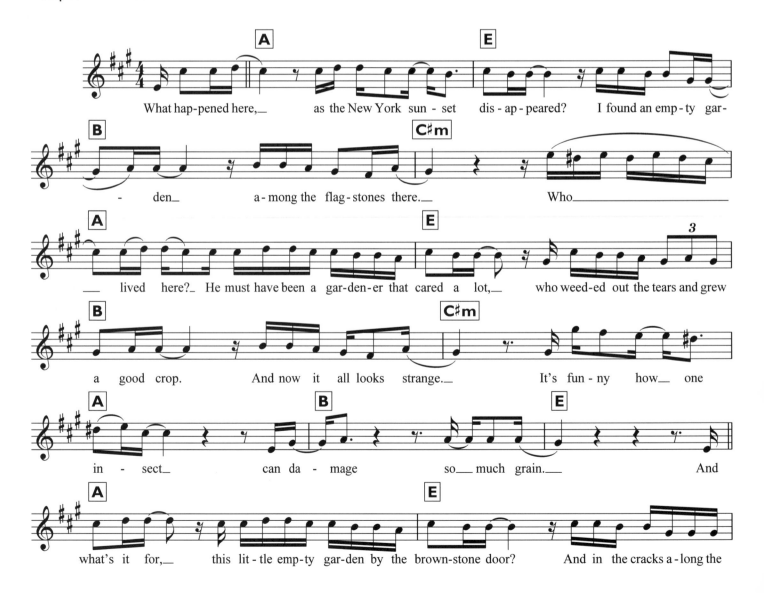

HEALING HANDS

Words & Music by Elton John & Bernie Taupin

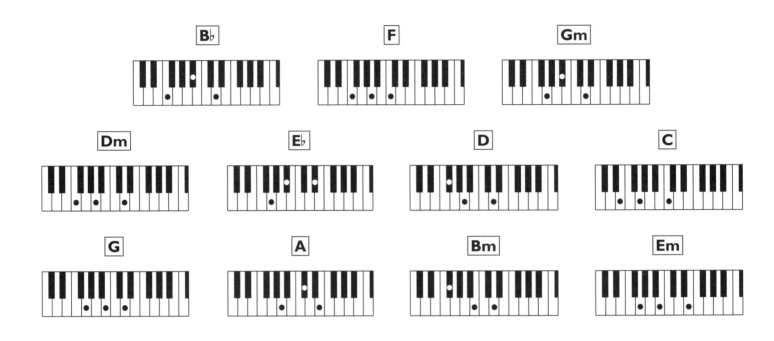

Voice: **New Age Pad**

Rhythm: **Rock 2**

Tempo: ♩ = 114

I never dreamed_ I could cry so hard._ That ain't like a man.

I could fly like a bird some___ days._ Had a

place where I could_ land._____ I could have sworn we were

I WANT LOVE

Words & Music by Elton John & Bernie Taupin

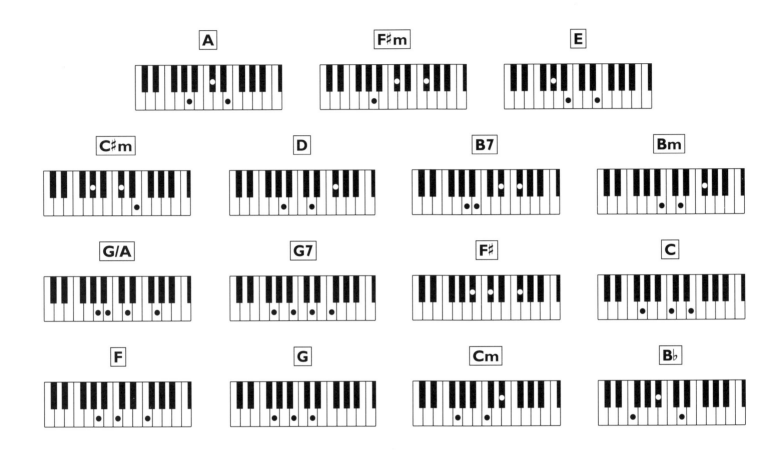

Voice:	**Tenor Saxophone**
Rhythm:	**Slow Rock**
Tempo:	♩ = 72

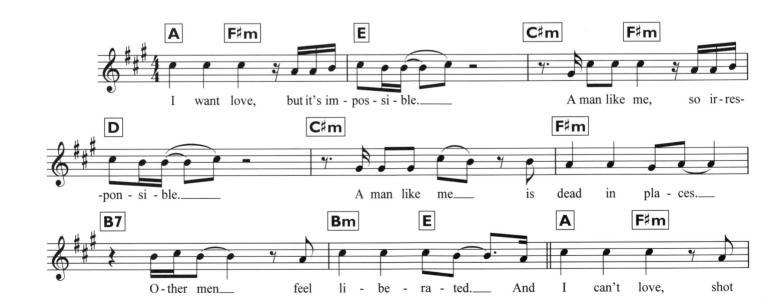

INDIAN SUNSET

Words & Music by Elton John & Bernie Taupin

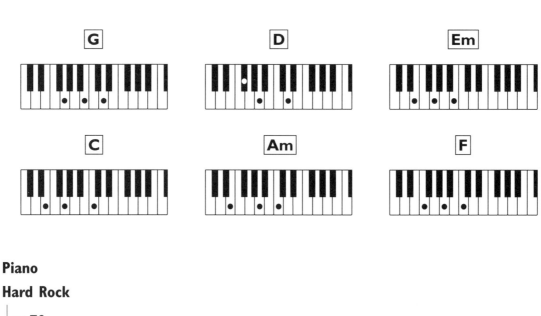

Voice: **Piano**

Rhythm: **Hard Rock**

Tempo:  ♩ = 70

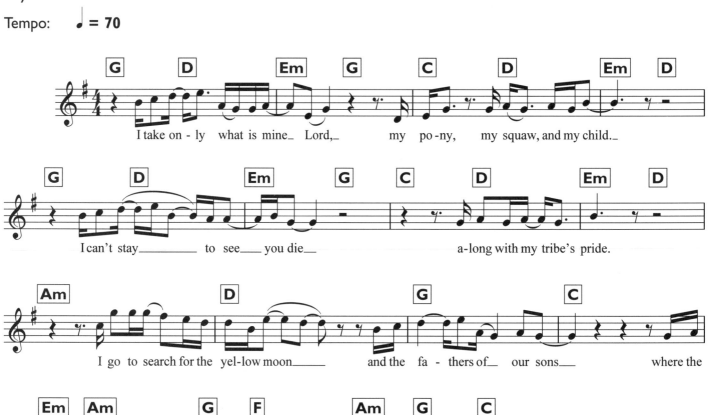

I take on - ly what is mine Lord, my po - ny, my squaw, and my child.

I can't stay to see you die a-long with my tribe's pride.

I go to search for the yel-low moon and the fa - thers of our sons where the

red sun sinks in the hills of gold and the heal - ing wa - ters run.

Tramp-ling down the prai - rie rose leav-ing hoof tracks in the sand.

KISS THE BRIDE

Words & Music by Elton John & Bernie Taupin

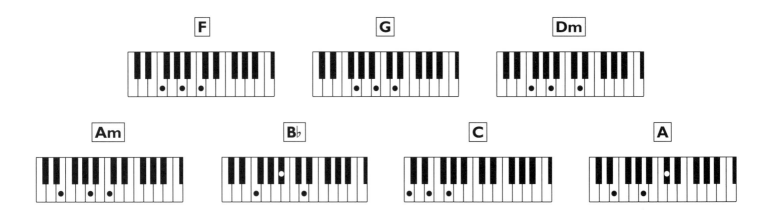

Voice: **Electric Guitar**

Rhythm: **Straight Rock**

Tempo: ♩ = 138

Well she looked a peach in the dress she made when she was

still her ma-ma's lit-tle girl.___ And when she walked down the aisle ev-'ry-

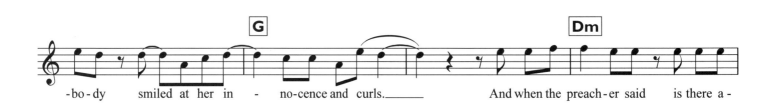

-bo-dy smiled at her in - no-cence and curls.___ And when the preach-er said is there a-

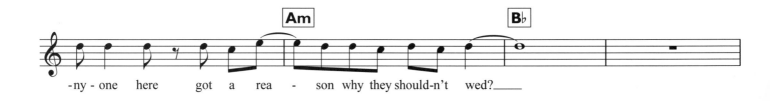

-ny-one here got a rea - son why they should-n't wed?___

I should have stuck up my hand.___ I should have got up to stand.___

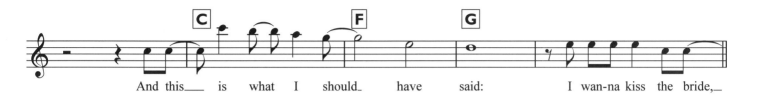

And this___ is what I should___ have said: I wan-na kiss the bride,___

___ yeah! I wan-na kiss the bride,___ yeah!

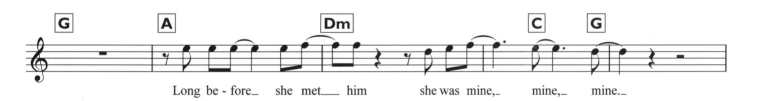

Long be-fore___ she met___ him she was mine,___ mine,___ mine.___

Don't say___ "I do",___ say "bye,___ bye, bye!"_____

And let me kiss the bride___ yeah!

Repeat to fade

I wan-na kiss the bride___ yeah!

LEVON

Words & Music by Elton John & Bernie Taupin

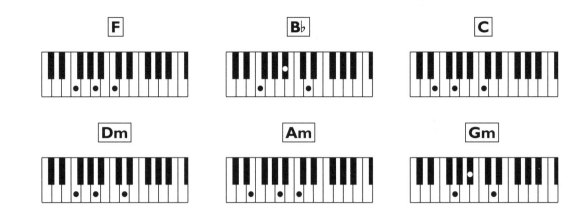

Voice: **Rock Organ**

Rhythm: **Rock**

Tempo: ♩ = 72

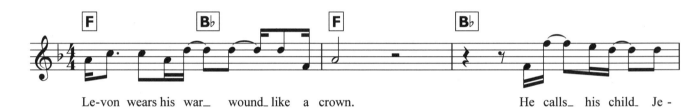

Le-von wears his war_ wound_ like a crown.   He calls_ his child_ Je-

- sus_____   'cause he likes_ the name_____   and he

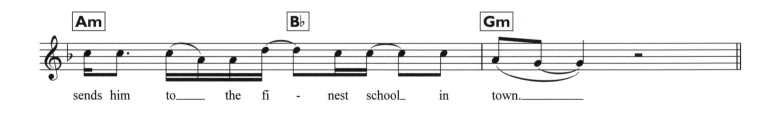

sends him to_ the fi - nest school_ in town._

Le-von,   Le-von likes his mo - ney._   He makes_ a lot,_ they

THE ONE

Words & Music by Elton John & Bernie Taupin
© Copyright 1991 Universal Music Publishing Limited.
All rights in Germany administered by Universal Music Publ. GmbH.
All Rights Reserved. International Copyright Secured.

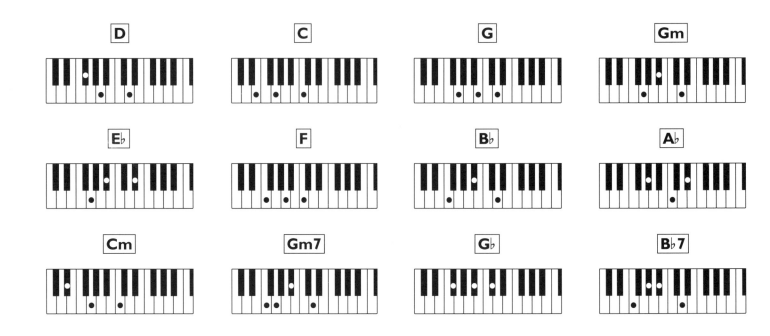

Voice: **Electric Piano**

Rhythm: **16 Rock**

Tempo: ♩ = 76

PART-TIME LOVE

Words & Music by Elton John & Gary Osborne

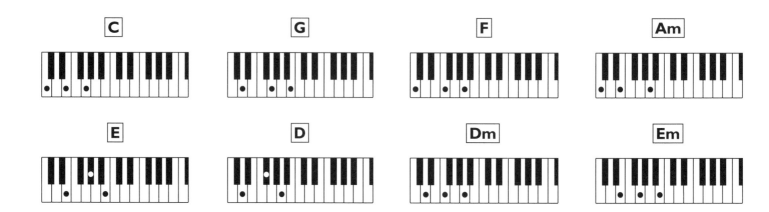

Voice: **Electric Guitar**

Rhythm: **Hard Rock**

Tempo: ♩ = 142

Part - time love is bring-ing me down 'cause I just can't get start-ed with you,

my love. Did I hear you say - ing that I'm too hard heart-ed?

Wipe those stars from your eyes and you'll get quite a sur - prise. Be-cause

you'll see e - ve-ry-bo - dy's got a part - time love.

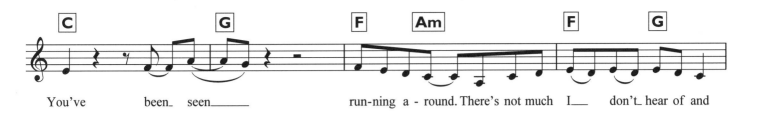

You've been seen running a - round. There's not much I don't hear of and

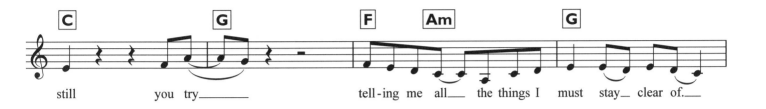

still you try telling me all the things I must stay clear of.

Don't tell me what to do when you've been doing it too. Be-cause

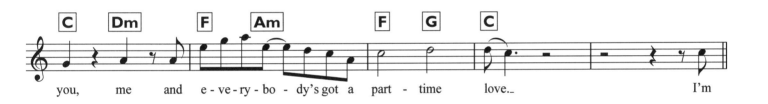

you, me and e - ve - ry - bo - dy's got a part - time love. I'm

fall - ing, I'm fall - ing can't get free, ba - by, if you

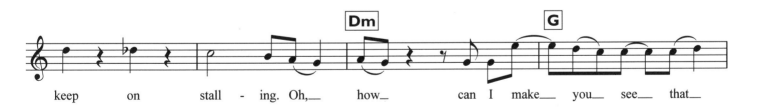

keep on stall - ing. Oh, how can I make you see that

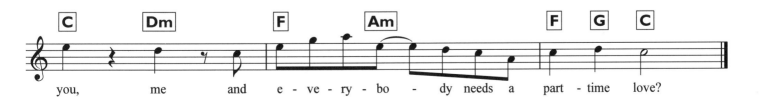

you, me and e - ve - ry - bo - dy needs a part - time love?

PHILADELPHIA FREEDOM

Words & Music by Elton John & Bernie Taupin

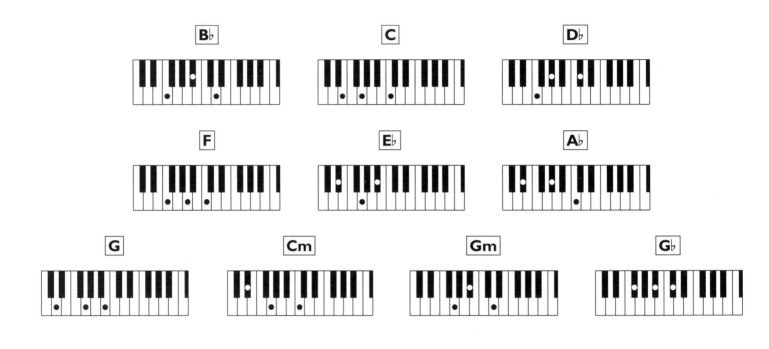

Voice: **Electric Guitar**

Rhythm: **Hard Rock**

Tempo: ♩ = 125

I used to be a roll-ing stone, you know, if the cause was right. I'd leave

to find the ans-wer on the road. I

used to be a heart beat-ing for some-one. But the times have changed:

The less I say the more my work gets done. 'Cause I

SAD SONGS (SAY SO MUCH)

Words & Music by Elton John & Bernie Taupin

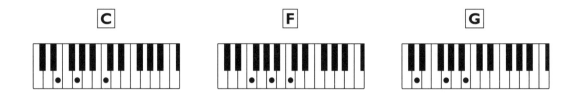

Voice: **Electric Piano**

Rhythm: **Disco Pop**

Tempo: ♩ = 104

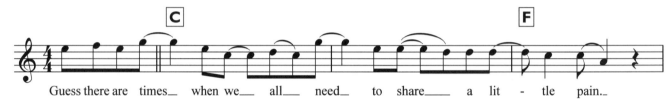

Guess there are times＿ when we＿ all＿ need＿ to share＿ a lit - tle pain.＿

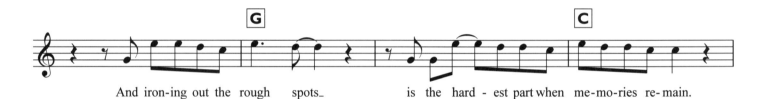

And iron-ing out the rough spots＿ is the hard - est part when me-mo-ries re-main.

And it's times＿ like these＿ when we all＿ need to hear＿ the ra - di - o.＿

'Cause from the lips of some＿ old sing - er we can share the trou-bles we al-rea-dy know.

Turn them on,＿＿ turn them on,＿＿ turn on those sad songs.＿

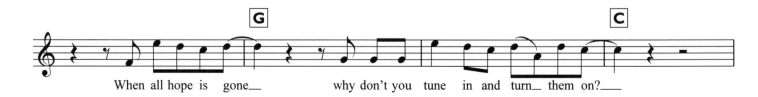

When all hope is gone＿ why don't you tune in and turn＿ them on?＿＿

SOMEONE SAVED MY LIFE TONIGHT

Words & Music by Elton John & Bernie Taupin

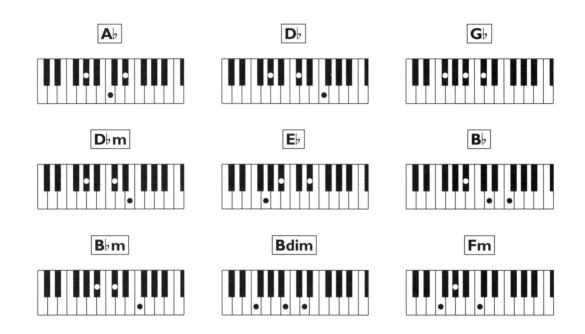

Voice: **Flute**

Rhythm: **Slow Rock**

Tempo: ♩ = **72**

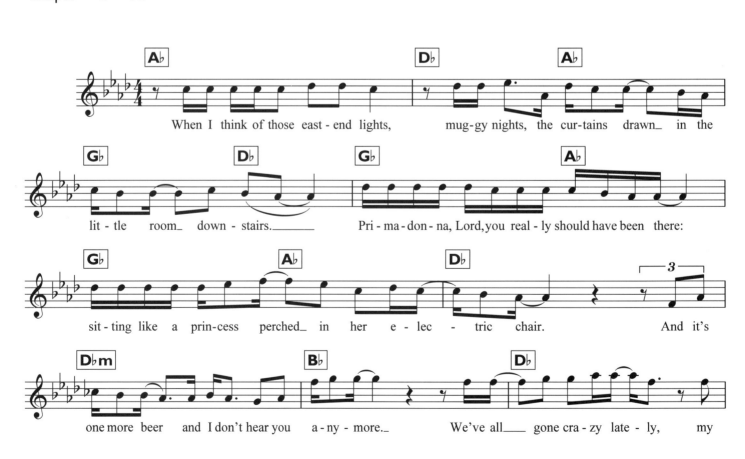

When I think of those east-end lights, mug-gy nights, the cur-tains drawn in the lit-tle room down-stairs. Pri-ma-don-na, Lord, you real-ly should have been there: sit-ting like a prin-cess perched in her e-lec-tric chair. And it's one more beer and I don't hear you a-ny-more. We've all gone cra-zy late-ly, my

friends out there_ roll - ing 'round_ the base - ment floor._

And some-one_ saved my life to - night,_ su - gar bear._ You al - most had your hooks in me,_

didn't you dear?_ You near-ly had me roped_ and tied,_ al - tar - bound, hyp-no - tized._ Sweet free-

- dom whis-pered in__ my ear "You're a but-ter-fly"._ And but-ter-flies_ are free_ to fly,_

fly a - way,_ high a - way,_ bye_ bye. Oooh...__

And I would have walked_ head on__ in - to the deep end of the ri - ver,

cling-ing to your stocks and bonds,__ pay-ing your H. P. de-mands for - e - ver.

They're com-ing in the morn - ing with_ a truck_ to take_ me home._

Repeat to fade

Some-one saved my life_ to - night._ Some-one saved my life_ to - night._

SOMETHING ABOUT THE WAY YOU LOOK TONIGHT

Words & Music by Elton John & Bernie Taupin

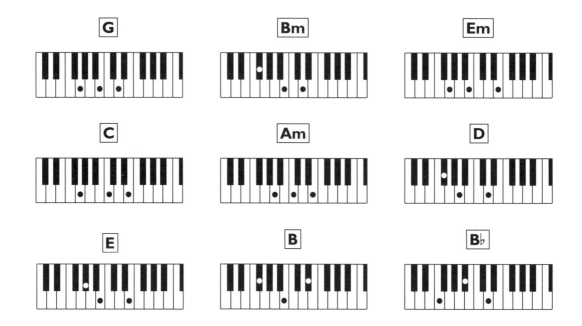

Voice: **Electric Guitar**

Rhythm: **Rock 2**

Tempo: ♩ = 72

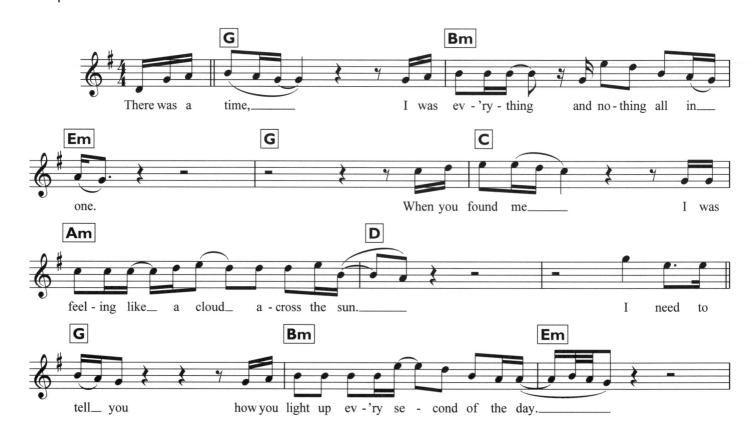

There was a time,_____ I was ev-'ry-thing and no-thing all in___ one.

When you found me_____ I was feel-ing like__ a cloud__ a-cross the sun._____ I need to tell__ you how you light up ev-'ry se - cond of the day._____

SORRY SEEMS TO BE THE HARDEST WORD

Words & Music by Elton John & Bernie Taupin

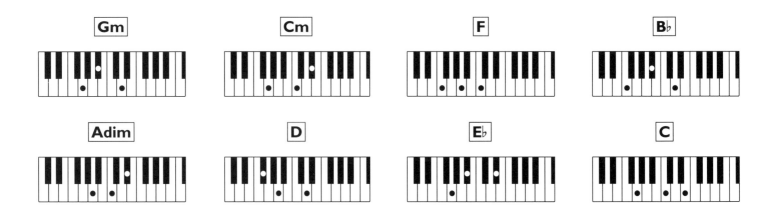

Voice: **Accordion**

Rhythm: **R&B Ballad**

Tempo: ♩ = 72

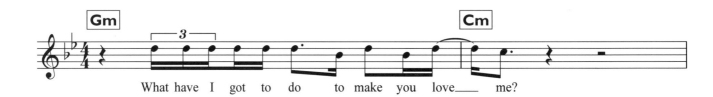

What have I got to do to make you love___ me?

What have I got to do___ to make you care?___

What do I do when light-ning strikes___ me

and I wake to find___ that you're_ not there?

What do I do to make you want_ me?   What have I got to do___ to_ be heard?_

THIS TRAIN DON'T STOP THERE ANYMORE

Words & Music by Elton John & Bernie Taupin

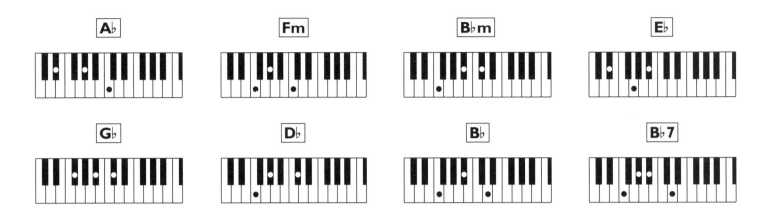

Voice: **Honky-Tonk Piano**

Rhythm: **Pop Ballad**

Tempo: ♩. = 102

You may not be-lieve it but I don't be-lieve in mi-rac-les a-ny-more.

And when I think a-bout it I don't be-lieve I e-ver did for sure.

All the things I've said in songs, all the pur-ple prose you

bought from me:___ Re - a - li-ty's just black and white. The

sen - ti - men-tal things I'd write ne-ver meant that much to me. I

used to be the main ex-press,___ all steam and whist-les head-ing west.___

TINY DANCER

Words & Music by Elton John & Bernie Taupin

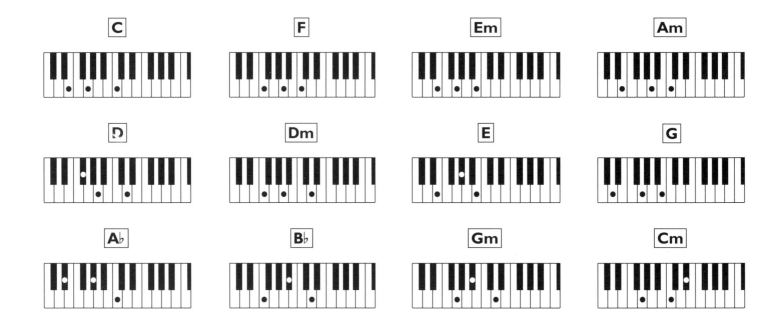

Voice: **Honky-Tonk Piano**

Rhythm: **Pop Rock**

Tempo: ♩ = 72

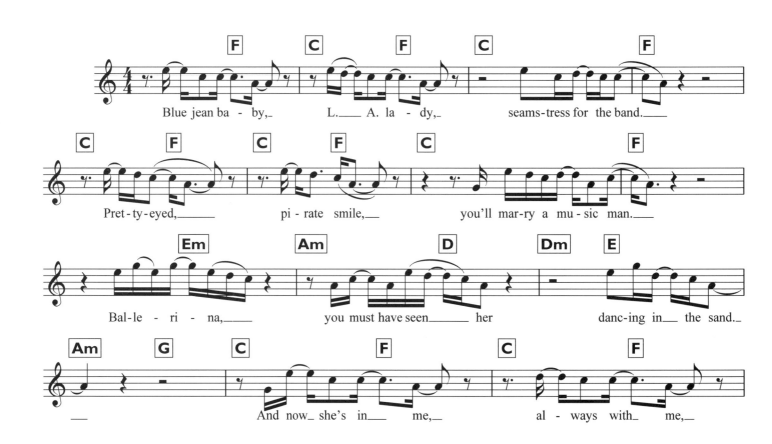

YOU GOTTA LOVE SOMEONE

Words & Music by Elton John & Bernie Taupin

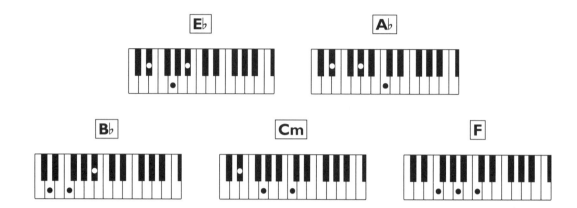

Voice:	**Electric Guitar**
Rhythm:	**Latin Pop**
Tempo:	♩ = 102

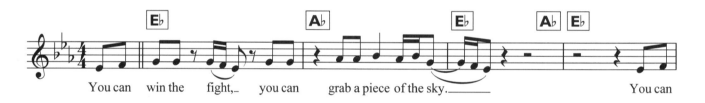

You can win the fight,_ you can grab a piece of the sky._____ You can

break the_ rules,_ mmm, but be-fore you try_____ you got-ta love_

_ some-one. You got-ta love_ some-one. You can

stop the_ world,_ steal the face from the moon._____ You can

EASIEST KEYBOARD COLLECTION

Easy-to-play melody line arrangements for all keyboards with chord symbols and lyrics. Suggested registration, rhythm and tempo are included for each song together with keyboard diagrams showing left-hand chord voicings used.

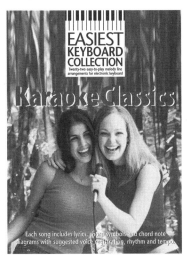

Karaoke Classics

The Best (Tina Turner),
Crazy (Patsy Cline),
Girls Just Want To Have Fun (Cyndi Lauper),
Hero (Enrique Iglesias),
Like A Prayer (Madonna),
(I've Had) The Time Of My Life (Bill Medley & Jennifer Warnes),
Like A Prayer (Madonna)
and 15 more big karaoke hits.
Order No. AM985072

Classics

Barcarolle (Offenbach),
Caprice No.21 (Paganini),
and 20 more classic themes,
including New World Symphony (Dvořák),
Ode To Joy from Symphony No.9 (Beethoven),
Spring from *The Four Seasons* (Vivaldi), and
Swan Lake (Tchaikovsky).
Order No. AM952094

Christmas Hits

Over 20 favourite festive hits,
including All I Want For Christmas Is You (Mariah Carey),
Blue Christmas (Elvis Presley),
I Saw Mommy Kissing Santa Claus (The Ronettes),
Lonely This Christmas (Mud),
and Walking In The Air – Theme from *The Snowman* (Aled Jones).
Order No. AM986964

Hits 2005

A great collection of 22 chart h
of 2005, including
Filthy/Gorgeous (Scissor Sisters),
Radio (Robbie Williams),
Room On The Third Floor (McF
Shiver (Natalie Imbruglia),
This Is The Last Time (Keane),
What You Waiting For (Gwen Stefani),
and Wisemen (James Blunt).
Order No. AM91982

Over 50 titles available in this series

Abba, Order No. AM959860
Ballads, Order No. AM952116
The Beatles, Order No. NO90686
Broadway, Order No. AM952127
Chart Hits, Order No. AM952083
Classic Blues, Order No. AM950697
The Corrs, Order No. AM959849
Elvis Presley, Order No. AM959882

Film Themes, Order No. AM952050
Jazz Classics, Order No. AM952061
Latin, Order No. AM955834
Robbie Williams, Order No. AM972444
60s Hits, Order No. AM955768
70s Hits, Order No. AM968132
80s Hits, Order No. AM955779
90s Hits, Order No. AM944229

...plus many more!